Rescue at sea

Written by Jill Atkins

Illustrated by Shelagh McNicholas

Heinemann

In the summer Alison went to stay
with her gran and grandad in
Scotland. One day Alison wanted
to see the fishing boats. She asked
Jamie, the boy who lived next
door, to go with her.
'I can't,' said Jamie. 'I have to
stay in and help my mum.'

So Alison went with her grandad
to see the fishing boats. It was
raining but they could just about
see the boats coming in. Alison
looked through Grandad's
binoculars.

'I can see six boats coming in,'
she said.

Alison ran down the jetty to look at
the boats. The first boat had come
in and the men were carrying boxes
of fish on to the jetty.

'Herring! Come and buy! Best herring!'
a fisherman shouted very loudly.

'I'll have six, please,' said Grandad.
The man put the herrings in a bag.

Just then four other boats came in.
Alison heard two fishermen talking.
'The waves are getting bigger and
bigger,' said one man, 'and Tom's
boat hasn't come in.'
'He should be back by now,' said
the other man.

Alison ran back to Grandad.

'One of the boats hasn't come back,' she told him. 'I heard two fishermen talking.'

'I hope it will be here soon,' said Grandad.

'So do I,' said Alison.

Alison looked out to sea. She could see something.

She looked through the binoculars.
Now she could see a boat going up
and down on the waves.
'Grandad! Come and
look,' she shouted.
'The wind is blowing
the boat on to the rocks.'

'We must call the lifeboat,' said
Grandad. 'Run, Alison! You're faster
than me.'
So Alison ran along the jetty as fast
as she could.

She called the
coastguard and
told him about
the boat.

Soon some men ran into the lifeboat station. Then Alison saw the big doors open and the lifeboat set off to help the fishing boat.

'I hope they get there in time,' she said.

Alison went back to Grandad.
She looked through the binoculars.
She saw the lifeboat get to the
fishing boat. Then she saw the
lifeboat men help the fishermen
off their boat.

When the last fisherman was in
the lifeboat it turned and came
back through the waves. Just then
the fishing boat went CRASH
on to the rocks.

When the lifeboat got back to the jetty the men went off to get warm and dry. The lifeboat was put away.

The captain came over to Grandad.
'It was thanks to you that we got to
the men in time,' he said.
'Don't thank me,' said Grandad.
'Thank Alison. She was the first one
to see the boat.'

When Alison and Grandad got home
Alison went to see Jamie.

'I called out the lifeboat,' said Alison.

'I know,' said Jamie. 'My dad and I
want to thank you because my dad
was on that fishing boat!'